有趣的英文歌曲

Exciting English Songs.

風車圖書(版)

Hokey – Pokey

You put your ① right hand in. You put your right hand out.

You put your right hand in and you shake it all about.

You do the hokey-pokey and you turn yourself around.

That's what it's all about!

② left hand ③ right foot ④ left foot ⑤ telling part ⑥ whole self

變戲法

把①右手放進來，再把右手伸出去。
把①右手放進來，盡情的搖動，
一邊變戲法，一邊轉圈圈。
那就是戲法的全部呀！
② 左手　③ 右腳　④ 左腳　⑤ 說到部分　⑥ 全身

One elephant went out to play

One elephant went out to play out on a spider's web one day.

He had such enormous fun. He called for another elephant to come.

Two elephants went out to play out on a spider's web one day.

They had such enormous fun. They called for another elephant to come.

Three elephants went out to play out on a spider's web one day.

They had such enormous fun. They called for another elephant to come.

Four elephants went out to play out on a spider's web one day.

They had such enormous fun. They called for another elephant to come.

Five elephants went out to play out on a spider's web one day.

They had such enormous fun.

They called for another elephant to come.

一隻大象出去玩

有天，一隻大象出去玩，被蜘蛛網勾到了，
因為實在太有趣了，牠叫其它大象一起玩，
有天，二隻大象出去玩，被蜘蛛網勾到了，
因為實在太有趣了，牠們叫其它大象一起玩，
有天，三隻大象出去玩，被蜘蛛網勾到了，
因為實在太有趣了，牠們叫其它大象一起玩。

有天，四隻大象出去玩，被蜘蛛網勾到了，
因為實在太有趣了，牠們叫其它大象一起玩。
有天，五隻大象出去玩，被蜘蛛網勾到了，
因為實在太有趣了，牠們叫其它大象一起玩。

8

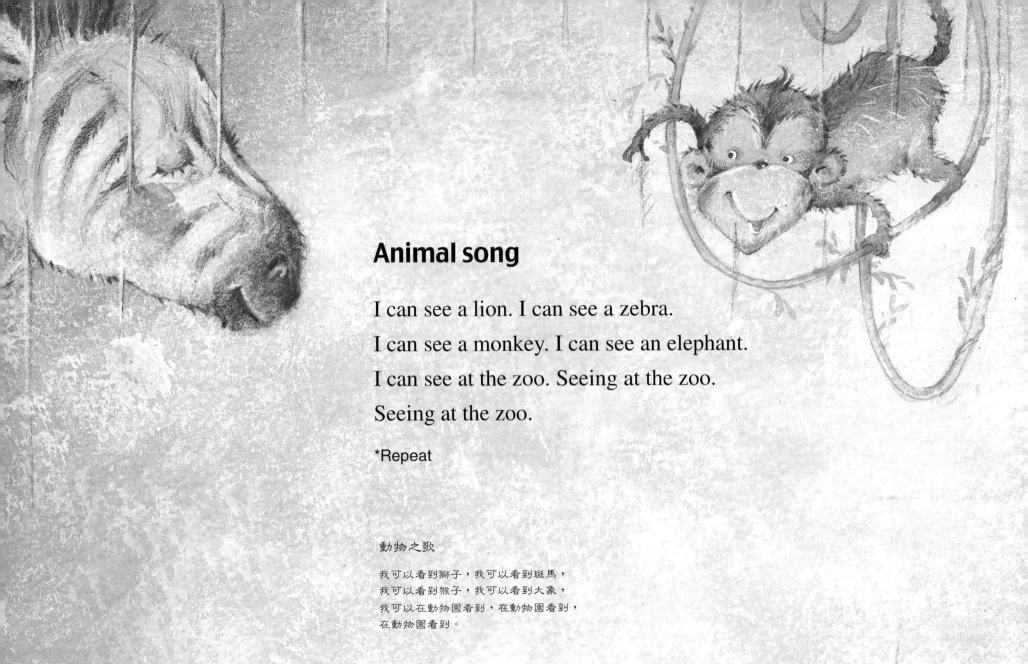

Animal song

I can see a lion. I can see a zebra.

I can see a monkey. I can see an elephant.

I can see at the zoo. Seeing at the zoo.

Seeing at the zoo.

*Repeat

動物之歌

我可以看到獅子，我可以看到斑馬，
我可以看到猴子，我可以看到大象，
我可以在動物園看到，在動物園看到，
在動物園看到。

Tick–Tock

Tick-Tock Tick-Tock Tick-Tock goes the clock.

Tick-Tock Tick-Tock Tick-Tock goes the clock.

One o'clock, two o'clock, three o'clock it never stops.

Four o'clock, five o'clock, six o'clock, Tick-Tock.

Tick-Tock Tick-Tock Tick-Tock goes the clock.

Tick-Tock Tick-Tock Tick-Tock goes the clock.

Seven o'clock, eight o'clock, nine o'clock it never stops.

Ten o'clock, eleven o'clock, twelve o'clock, Tick-Tock.

Tick-Tock Tick-Tock Tick-Tock goes the clock.

Tick-Tock Tick-Tock Tick-Tock goes the clock.

One, two, three, four, five, six, seven, eight, and nine,

and then, ten, eleven, twelve, again round o'clock Tick-Tock.

Tick-Tock Tick-Tock Tick-Tock goes the clock.

Tick-Tock Tick-Tock Tick-Tock goes the clock.

滴答滴答

滴答滴答滴答　時間在走耶！
滴答滴答滴答　時間在走耶！
一點、二點、三點，一刻不停留，
四點、五點、六點，滴答！
滴答滴答滴答　時間在走耶！
滴答滴答滴答　時間在走耶！

七點、八點、九點，一刻也不停留，
十點、十一點、十二點，滴答！
滴答滴答滴答　時間在走耶！
滴答滴答滴答　時間在走耶！

1，2，3，4，5，6，7，8跟9，
接著是10，11，12，繞轉了一圈，滴答！
滴答滴答滴答　時間在走耶！
滴答滴答滴答　時間在走耶！

Counting song

One, two, three, four, one, two, three, four,

Five, six, seven, eight, five, six, seven, eight.

One, two, three, four, five, six, seven, eight,

nine, ten.

*Repeat

數字歌

一，二，三，四，一，二，三，四，
五，六，七，八，五，六，七，八，
一，二，三，四，五，六，七，八，
九，十。

13

Thank you!

Thanks! Thank you! Thank you so much!

Thank you very much! You are welcome!

Thanks! Thanks! Thanks a lot!

You are welcome! You are welcome!

*Repeat

謝謝你！

謝謝！謝謝你！真是謝謝你！
非常謝謝你！不客氣！
謝謝！謝謝你！十分謝謝你！
不客氣！不客氣！

Hello song

Hello, Hello, Hello. What's your name?
Hello, Hello, Hello.
My name is John. My name is John.
Hello John. Hello John. Hello.

Hello, Hello, Hello. What's your name?
Hello, Hello, Hello.
My name is Kate. My name is Kate.
Hello Kate. Hello Kate. Hello.

問候歌

哈囉，哈囉，哈囉，你叫什麼名字呢？
哈囉，哈囉，哈囉。
我的名字叫約翰，我的名字叫約翰。
哈囉，約翰。哈囉，約翰。哈囉。

哈囉，哈囉，哈囉，你叫什麼名字呢？
哈囉，哈囉，哈囉。
我的名字叫凱蒂，我的名字叫凱蒂。
哈囉，凱蒂。哈囉，凱蒂。哈囉。

How old are you?

How old are you? How old are you? I'm eleven. I'm eleven.

How old are you? How old are you? I'm eleven, eleven.

How old are you? How old are you? I'm eleven years old.

How old are you? How old are you? I'm eleven years old.

*Repeat

你幾歲？

你幾歲？你幾歲？我１１歲，我１１歲了。
你幾歲？你幾歲？１１歲，我１１歲了。
你幾歲？你幾歲？我１１歲了。
你幾歲？你幾歲？我１１歲了。

What's this?

What's this? What's this? What's this? What? What?
It's a hat. It's a hat. It's a hat, hat, hat.

What's that? What's that? What's that? What? What?
It's a ball. It's a ball. It's a ball, ball, ball.

這是什麼？

這是什麼？這是什麼？這是什麼呢？什麼？什麼呢？
這是帽子，這是帽子，這是帽子、帽子、帽子。

那是什麼？那是什麼？那是什麼呢？什麼？什麼呢？
那是球，那是球，那是球、球、球。

19

Open shut them

Open shut them, Open shut them, give a little clap clap clap.

Open shut them, Open shut them, put them on your lap. (*Repeat)

Open shut them, Open shut them, give a little clap clap clap.

Open shut them, Open shut them, put them on your eyes. (*Repeat)

Roll them, Roll them, Roll them, Roll them, give a little clap clap clap.

Roll them, Roll them, Roll them, Roll them, put them on your head. (*Repeat)

Roll them, Roll them, Roll them, Roll them, give a little clap clap clap.

Roll them, Roll them, Roll them, Roll them, put them behind you. (*Repeat)

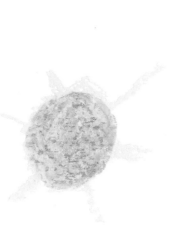

張開手拍拍手

張開手拍拍手，張開手拍拍手，小小聲地啪、啪、啪。
張開手拍拍手，張開手拍拍手，把手放在膝蓋上。
張開手拍拍手，張開手拍拍手，小小聲地啪、啪、啪。
張開手拍拍手，張開手拍拍手，把手放在眼睛上。

擺擺手，擺擺手，擺擺手，擺擺手，小小聲地啪、啪、啪
擺擺手，擺擺手，擺擺手，擺擺手，把手放在你頭上。
擺擺手，擺擺手，擺擺手，擺擺手，小小聲地啪、啪、啪。
擺擺手，擺擺手，擺擺手，擺擺手，把手放在你身後。

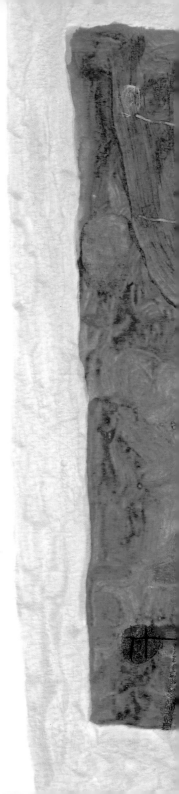

21

The Marching band

We are the Marching band. We are the Marching band.

I can play the Flute. I can play the Castanets.

I can play the glockenspiel. I can play the Snare drum.

We are the Marching band. We are the Marching band.

I can play the trumpet. I can play the tambourine.

I can play the trombone. I can play the bass drum.

We are the Marching band. We are the Marching band.

We are the Marching band. We are the Marching band.

We are the Marching band.

音樂隊

我們是音樂隊，我們是音樂隊。
我會吹笛子，我會敲響板，
我會敲鐘琴，我會打小鼓。
我們是音樂隊，我們是音樂隊。
我會吹喇叭，我會搖鈴鼓，
我會吹伸縮喇叭，我會打大鼓。
我們是音樂隊，我們是音樂隊。
我們是音樂隊，我們是音樂隊，
我們是音樂隊。

I can! I can!

I can skate and I can swim. I can skate and I can swim.
I can skate and I can swim. Lucky me. Oh! Lucky me.
I can hop and I can dance. I can hop and I can dance.
I can hop and I can dance. Lucky me. Oh! Lucky me.

I can read and I can write. I can read and I can write.
I can read and I can write. Lucky me. Oh! Lucky me.

我會！我會！

我會溜冰，也會游泳。我會溜冰，也會游泳。
我會溜冰，也會游泳。我真幸運，喔！真幸運！
我會跳，也會跳舞。我會跳，也會跳舞。
我會跳，也會跳舞。我真幸運，喔！真幸運！

我會讀書，也會寫字。我會讀書，也會寫字。
我會讀書，也會寫字。我真幸運，喔！真幸運！

Long Vowel song

Let's sing a long vowel song.

A A A Angel, Angel, Angel.

E E E Evening, Evening, Evening.

I I I Ice-cream, Ice-cream, Ice-cream.

O O O O.K. O.K. O.K.

U U U U Unicorn, Unicorn, Unicorn.

*Repeat

長母音歌

我們來唱長母音歌，

A A A 天使，天使，天使。

E E E 晚安，晚安，晚安。

I I I 冰淇淋，冰淇淋，冰淇淋。

O O O O.K. O.K. O.K.

U U U U 獨角獸，獨角獸，獨角獸。

26

Sorry! Sorry! Sorry!

Sorry! Sorry! Sorry! I'm sorry! I'm sorry!

That's all right. That's all right.

Sorry! Sorry! I'm sorry! That's all right.

*Repeat

對不起！對不起！對不起！

對不起！對不起！對不起！真是對不起！
我真是對不起！
沒關係，沒關係！
對不起！對不起！真是對不起！沒關係！

27

I have to wait for '

I have to wait for my friend. I have to wait for my friend.

We are playing tennis and my friend isn't coming.

I have to wait for my friend.

*Repeat

我要等…

我要等我的朋友，我要等我的朋友。
我們要打網球，但是我的朋友還沒來，
我要等我的朋友。

29

Singing all day long

Every morning when I wake up. The birds out side my window.

Say good-morning wake up wake up. It's time to sing a song.

Have a singing all day long.

Singing la la la la la la la la la la. Singing all day long.

Singing la la la la la la la la la la. Singing all day long.

In my court and in the trees. And in the grassy meadow.

Birds are singing so cheerfully. I love to sing along.

Have a singing all day long.

Singing la la la la la la la la la la. Singing all day long.

Singing la la la la la la la la la la. Singing all day long. (*Repeat)

歡唱一整天

每天清晨當我睜開眼，鳥兒就在我窗外，
叫我起床跟我說早安，歌唱時刻已來到，
歡唱一整天。
啦啦啦啦啦啦啦啦啦啦，歡唱一整天。
啦啦啦啦啦啦啦啦啦啦，歡唱一整天。

在家附近的樹上，在那青綠草地上，
鳥兒喜悅地歌唱，我愛隨著齊聲唱。
歡唱一整天。
啦啦啦啦啦啦啦啦啦啦，歡唱一整天。
啦啦啦啦啦啦啦啦啦啦，歡唱一整天。

My Boat

My boat's sailing, sailing ,sailing.

My boat's sailing over the water.

My boat's sailing, sailing ,sailing.

My boat's sailing over the sea.

Will you go with me? Will you go with me?

Will you go with me over the water?

Yes, I go with you. Yes, I go with you.

Yes, I go with you over the sea.

*Repeat

我的船

我的船啟航了，啟航了，啟航了。
我的船越過了江，
我的船啟航了，啟航了，啟航了。
我的船越過了海。
你要跟我一起航行嗎？你要跟我一起航行嗎？
你要跟我一起越過江嗎？
是的，我要跟你一起航行。是的，我要跟你一起航行。
是的，我要跟你一起越過海。

My puppy

I have a puppy. This is my puppy.
You have a puppy. That is your puppy.
Yes, Yes. It is my my my puppy.

I have a kitten. This is my kitten.
You have a kitten. That is your kitten.
Yes, Yes. It is your your your Kitten.

34

我的小狗

我有一隻小狗，這是我的小狗。
你有一隻小狗，那是你的小狗。
是的，是的。牠是我的，我的，我的小狗。

我有一隻小貓，這是我的小貓。
你有一隻小貓，那是你的小貓。
是的，是的。牠是你的，你的，你的小貓。

35

Everyday in the morning

This is the way I wash my face,
wash my face, wash my face.
This is the way I wash my face
everyday in the morning.

This is the way I brush my teeth,
brush my teeth, brush my teeth.
This is the way I brush my teeth
everyday in the morning.

每天清晨

我是這樣洗臉的，洗臉，洗臉。
每天清晨我是這樣洗臉的。
我是這樣刷牙的，刷牙，刷牙。
每天清晨我是這樣刷牙的。
我是這樣打掃房間的，打掃房間，打掃房間。
每天清晨我是這樣打掃房間的。
我是這樣看電視的，看電視，看電視。
每天清晨我是這樣看電視的。

This is the way I clean my room,
clean my room, clean my room.
This is the way I clean my room
everyday in the morning.

This is the way I watch TV,
watch TV, watch TV.
This is the way I watch TV
everyday in the morning.

Six little ducks

Six little ducks that I once knew.

Fat one, skinny one they were, too.

*But the one little duck with the feathers on his back.

He led the others with a quack, quack, quack!

Quack, quack, quack! quack, quack, quack!

He led the others with a quack, quack, quack!

Down by the river they would go,

Wibble-wobble, wibble-wobble, to and fro. (*Repeat)

Home from the river they would come,

Wibble-wobble, Wibble-wobble, ho-ho-hum! (*Repeat)

六隻小鴨

我所認識的六隻小鴨，
胖的小鴨，瘦的小鴨，都有耶！

但背部長羽毛的只有一隻，
呱呱呱地帶領著其他小鴨，
呱！呱！呱！呱！呱！呱！
呱呱呱地帶領著其他小鴨！

走到河邊小鴨們下水去，
搖搖晃晃，搖搖晃晃，來回地游。（※重覆）

離開河邊小鴨們要回家，
搖搖晃晃，搖搖晃晃，哼哼唱唱。（※重覆）

39

Good night

And now to all good night, good night, good night, good night.
And now to all good night, good night, good night, good night.

*Repeat

晚安

大家晚安，晚安，晚安，晚安！
大家晚安，晚安，晚安，晚安！

Goodbye

Goodbye! Goodbye, every body.

Goodbye! Goodbye, see you tomorrow.

Goodbye, Dick. Goodbye, Jane.

Goodbye! Goodbye! bye! bye! bye!

*Repeat

再見

再見！大家再見！
再見！再見！明天再見！
再見！迪克！再見，貞！
再見！再見！拜拜！拜拜！拜拜！

41

What's your favorite?

What's your favorite season, season?

I like winter. I like winter.

I like winter, winter, winter.

What's your favorite season, season?

I like spring. I like spring.

I like spring, spring, spring.

What's your favorite season, season?

I like summer. I like summer.

I like summer, summer, summer.

What's your favorite season, season?
I like fall. I like fall. I like fall, fall, fall.

你最愛的是什麼呢?

你最愛什麼季節?什麼季節呢?
我愛冬天。我愛冬天。
我最愛冬天、冬天、冬天。
你最愛什麼季節?什麼季節呢?
我愛春天。我愛春天。
我最愛春天、春天、春天。
你最愛什麼季節?什麼季節呢?
我愛夏天。我愛夏天。
我最愛夏天、夏天、夏天。
你最愛什麼季節?什麼季節呢?
我愛秋天。我愛秋天。
我最愛秋天、秋天、秋天。

Mozart's Lullaby

Sleep, little one go to sleep, so peaceful the birds and the sheep.

Quiet are meadow and trees, even the buzz of the bees.

The silvery moon beams so bright. Down through the window give light.

O'er you the moon beams will creep.

Sleep, little one go to sleep. Good night, Good night.

*Repeat

莫扎特搖籃曲

睡吧，我的寶貝。鳥兒和羊兒都靜靜地睡了。
草原與樹木寂靜無聲，蜜蜂的嗡嗡聲也停了。
銀色的月光那麼明亮，透過窗戶照射進來。
月光悄悄地爬上寶貝的床。
睡吧，我的寶貝。晚安！晚安！

有趣的英文歌曲

社長：許丁龍
繪圖：李雄基、夏賢里、金進鈴
編輯企畫：吳俊毅、吳鳳珠、邱月貞
出版：風車圖書出版有限公司
（局版北市業字第160號）
總代理：三暉圖書發行有限公司
地址：台北市114內湖區舊宗路二段107號4樓
電話：(02)2795-1436　傳真：(02)2794-5955
郵撥帳號：14957898
出版日期：2001年10月初版

Exciting
English Songs.